NING OF TIME

A n unimaginably long time ago – 15 billion or so years according to cosmologists and scientists – the Universe started with a big bang. It was the moment of creation when, within less than a second, all matter, energy, space and time exploded, from which beginning the Universe expanded and is still doing so. Before that moment of creation neither space nor time existed. So what was there when there was nothing? Many of the world's greatest brains and millions of lesser mortals have wrestled with this question. Some scientists believe that the answer is God, others that the question is still unanswerable.

MAIN PICTURE: *This is an artist's impression of the Big Bang, the primordial explosion which began everything. The theory of the Big Bang arose from astronomical observations that the visible Universe is expanding. The artist has shown the Universe just after the Big Bang when vast clouds of gas are beginning to condense into what will later become the millions of galaxies of stars that make up the Universe.*

Today our concept of time comes from the most advanced fields of astronomy and physics, but its true nature remains a mystery. Time is intangible and is called the fourth dimension, but that is a dimension which cannot be drawn. Clocks measure time as though it moves at a constant speed, but Einstein says that time in space is variable and relative to the beholder. How does time behave in other galaxies? Is it bent, as light is, by galaxies' gravitational fields?

Investigations to test Einstein's theory of relativity have found that, as the velocity of an object approaches the speed of light, its mass increases exponentially, its length reduces and time slows down. This means that if a space-ship were to fly at 99 per cent of the speed of light for one year, the astronauts on board would find that when they returned home, seven years had passed on Earth.

On a personal plane the speed of time is forever changing. It passes very slowly when we are young and speeds up as we get older. An hour is but a moment when we are enjoying ourselves or are very busy. For the prisoner in his cell, the lonely, the insomniac, it all but stops.

ABOVE: *Albert Einstein (1879–1955) questioned and redefined many of the basic concepts of physics, including the nature of time. He published his special theory of relativity in 1905 and his general theory in 1915.*

The nature of time has occupied great minds since classical days. The Greeks regarded time as being cyclic: when all the heavenly bodies return to the positions they occupied at the beginning, everything will be as it has been and then everything will start all over again. This theory was widespread in antiquity and was not much challenged until the early Christian leaders declared that the crucifixion was a unique event which could never be repeated, and therefore time was linear not cyclic. This is the current belief and it fits in with the theory of the Big Bang and the ever expanding Universe.

But there are proponents of a collapsing Universe theory who say that all matter will be pulled together into a finite mass and time will go back from where it came: nowhere. The German philosopher Kant would have nothing of that. He said time does not apply to the Universe, being only people's concept of the Universe.

RIGHT: *Sir Isaac Newton (1642–1727) was an English physicist and mathematician. He took the view that time existed independently of human minds and material objects, that it 'flowed' entirely on its own.*

LEFT: *St Augustine (354-430) said that the Crucifixion was a unique event and so set the Christian view of time.*

An artist's impression of warped space. Light normally travels in a straight line, but the gravity of enormous stars and black holes bends or warps light rays from their straight path. The denser the object the larger the dent it produces. Our Sun is shown below left but its dent is tiny compared with that of the black hole on the bottom right. The speed of light is a constant, so, if space is warped, time must also be warped by these dense masses.

TIME

BIOLOGICAL CLOCKS

Plants and animals are subject to natural rhythms. Certain plants do not open their petals or start the next step in their growth until a specific time of daylight has elapsed. Gardens can be cultivated to act as calendars and also to tell the time by the opening and closing of different blooms. Many sea creatures time their activities to the changing tides and some animals have biological clocks which tell them when to hibernate or migrate.

The human body left to its own devices is governed by natural interacting rhythms. The average adult heart beats 75 times a minute, body temperature, controlled by the hypothalamus, is lowest during the early morning after 1am. The female reproduction cycle takes about 28 days, imitating the Moon's phases.

RIGHT: The Evening Primrose has a very precise 'time clock': its flowers open between 6 and 7pm in early June, hence its name.

ASTRONOMEI

Early people must have wondered about the passing of time from observing the phenomena of sunrise and sunset, the waxing and waning of the Moon, and above all the cycle of birth, growth and death of all living things. Artifacts found in burial sites dating back 60,000 years suggest that people, even then, believed in life after death. The earliest records of people having a concept of time past, present and future are the Palaeolithic cave paintings of 20,000 to 10,000 BC.

By 25,000 BC Neolithic people were living in agricultural settlements growing crops and tending beasts. To survive they needed to know when to sow, when to reap, when the river would flood and when to expect drought and other natural occurrences of good and bad visitations. The wise men realized there was a right time for everything to happen, and that those times were related to the movements of the Moon, the Sun and some of the stars. They were the first astronomer priests.

Knowing nothing of science they saw the heavenly bodies as gods who controlled the seasons, the weather and every living thing. So they prescribed days when they should be pleaded with, praised or placated by ceremonials, festivals and sacrifices. And, gods willing, the priests could accurately tell the people what had to be done and when. Their knowledge of time gave them power over their people, and huge stone circles were built to help them predict the seasons.

There are more than 900 stone circles throughout Britain and many similar ones in Brittany. The exact reasons for their building and their functions are not fully known.

ABOVE: *The caves of Lascaux in France include the largest and richest prehistoric cavern containing paintings. People are thought to have started decorating the walls of Lascaux some 17,000 years ago (written history did not start for a further 12,000 years), and to have spent a few thousand years doing it. The paintings are the earliest works of art and recorded events of the past, the present*

PRIESTS

It is certain, however, that stone circles had some religious purpose and would therefore have been designed and used by the astronomer priests of the Neolithic and Bronze Age people, who needed some permanent means of marking the passing of time and the seasons. Astronomical alignments can be found on so many circles that they cannot all be coincidental and the circles must have been set up to be seasonal calendars.

ABOVE: *The high, bare and indented north-western coast of the Isle of Lewis is peppered with small stone circles and megaliths, the largest being the Standing Stones of Callanish. After lying hidden beneath the peat for thousands of years, they were uncovered in the last century.*

STONEHENGE

Stonehenge is the most famous stone circle. A sighting from the centre running out of the circle and up the middle of the broad processional causeway would see the rising Sun of the summer solstice floating just above the horizon, framed by the two sarsen stones of the monument's north-eastern entrance. Across the same broad axis are a number of stones, particularly the inward-leaning Heel stone, which were set up in alignment with specific phases of the Moon. The prehistoric astronomical priests, often misnamed Druids, must have been our first clock-makers.

MAIN PICTURE: *Long Meg dates from 1750 BC and is almost as old as the Egyptian pyramids. The stone was a prehistoric time marker for the winter solstice and the stone circle over which she stands was almost certainly a clock, or provided the parameters of a calendar, setting out the times for planting and reaping as well as the festivals of the religious or social year. The 'scientific' siting of Long Meg is given credence by the fact that her four angles are aligned to the four points of the compass, and that the winter solstice sun sets above her, as shown in the photo.*

Amongst the earliest calendar-makers were Sumerian priests who lived in about 3,000 BC. The ancients divided their calendars conveniently into twelve months each of thirty days representing the twelve new Moons which make up a year. Unfortunately their figures did not fit in with the movements of the Sun, or more accurately the Earth's journey around the Sun which takes 365.256 days. Nor did they fit with the interval from new Moon to new Moon which is 29 days 12 hours 44 minutes 2.87 seconds. Any calendar based on rounded solar or Moon numbers gets progressively out of date.

The Gregorian calendar, now used internationally, is descended from those of the Egyptian empire and the Romans. It was Julius Caesar who, in an attempt to make the perfect calendar, declared that every fourth year, now known as a

ABOVE: A 5th-century BC Babylonian calendar shows the lucky and unlucky days of the year. Each column represents a different month. The Babylonians used a seven-day week, with each day devoted to the worship of a different heavenly body – the Sun, the Moon, Mercury, Venus, Mars, Jupiter and Saturn. Many languages still base the names of some of the days of the week on the Babylonian gods.

CALENDARS

ABOVE: Every time we look at a calendar we should think of Julius Caesar, for it was he who introduced the Julian calendar on which ours is largely based. Before 1 January 45 BC when he brought the civil calendar into line with the astronomical year, the Roman calendar had been manipulated to such an extent for political reasons (to prolong a term of office, or bring forward an election) that it was three months out of phase with the seasons.

leap year, would have an extra day. The Roman calendar, however, still took on board an error in solar time and, to correct it, the Council of Nicaea which met in AD 325 put the date of the equinox back from 25 to 21 March and made Easter the first Sunday after the full Moon following 21 March.

By the end of the 16th century continuing error was putting Easter toward midsummer according to the Sun, rather than in spring. By decree of Pope Gregory, the year 1582 was shortened by ten days and it was decided that in future the last year of a century would not be made a leap year unless it was divisible by four hundred. Gregory's calendar is accurate to within one day in 3,323 years, an error which we have learned to live with!

It is, of course, a Christian calendar with the years dated from the birth of Christ with the prefix AD for Anno Domini, but even that timing is thought to be in error. The Julian calendar was originally dated from the founding of Rome and it was not until AD 527 that the Roman church introduced the present dating from Christ's birth. But historical evidence later placed His birth in 4 BC, which means that, to be accurate, we should have celebrated the millennium in 1996!

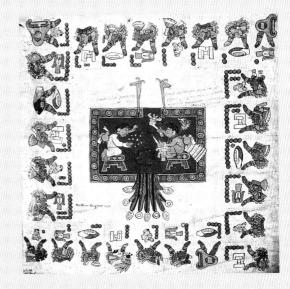

ABOVE: *An Aztec calendar. The Aztecs used two calendars – a religious one which had 260 days in a year and a solar one with 365 days in a year.*

This calendar is now used for all civil purposes but it took four centuries for it to be accepted by all countries. For religious purposes the Muslim calendar starts from the day Mohammed fled to Medina in AD 622 and the Jewish calendar dates back to the creation of the world, which they place at 3761 BC.

RIGHT: *Emperor Augustus (63 BC–AD 14) wanted a month named after him, with the same 31 days as Julius (July), so he took a day off February and tacked it onto the eighth month which he called August.*

LEFT: *In 1582 Pope Gregory XIII accepted the advice of a commission to adjust the Julian calendar and make it as accurate as it is today. The painting shows Pope Gregory discussing the reform of the Julian calendar.*

PRIMITIVE EGYPTIAN TIME-KEEPER

ABOVE: *This 1930s cigarette card shows an Ancient Egyptian sundial. The earliest known shadow clocks come from Egypt, a land with an almost cloudless sky.*

LEFT: *In the 16th and 17th centuries travel became a pastime of the leisured classes, and pocket sundials of silver, brass and ivory became fashionable accessories. The art of dialling or orientating sundials was taught in the better schools and universities. This folding pocket sundial was made in Germany and shows Italian hours, Babylonian hours and Jewish hours.*

As man developed industrially and socially he needed some means of measuring the time of day. Among the earliest clocks were shadow clocks (sundials) and water clocks developed in Egypt about 4,000 years ago. The shadow clocks were little more than a rod or bar which threw a shadow onto a semicircular time scale or stones indicating various times of the day. As the Sun moved from east to west, its shadow moved round, like the hour hand of a clock. When the Sun was overhead and the shadow shortest, it was noon.

Shadow clocks, or sundials as they came to be known, became very sophisticated and could tell the time to minutes and even seconds, and often gave other information such as the time of church services. There were also nocturnals or night dials for telling the time by moonlight. To be accurate a sundial must be designed for the latitude in which it will be used and then properly oriented using a compass. There is quite a science in dialling, as it is called, and most sundials supplied for gardens these days are useless for anything but decoration.

RIGHT: *The journey-ring or viatorium was an early navigational instrument which indicated latitude by the angle of the sun to the horizon using the sundial principle. It was used by Drake on his circumnavigation in 1577.*

LEFT: *The dials on this 16th-century Italian sundial show the time in Italian time which started a 24-hour day at sunset; in Babylonian time which started the 24-hour day at sunrise; and in Jewish time which divided the time between sunrise to sunset into 12 equal hours, regardless of the time of the year.*

SH

LIFE'S BUT A WALKING SHADOW

THIS IS LIFE ETERNAL THAT
THEY MAY KNOW THEE THE ONLY
TRUE GOD. AND JESUS CHRIST.
WHOM THOU HAST SENT.
ST JOHN, CHAPTER 17, VERSE 3.

ABOVE: *This sundial from the wall of Malmesbury House in Salisbury shows not only the time of day, but also the date on a Julian calendar.*

This famous obelisk, known as Cleopatra's Needle, was erected beside the River Thames in 1878, having been towed on a raft from Egypt. It originally stood in Heliopolis, and it is thought that such obelisks might have been the gnomons or shadow sticks of large sundials.

DOW CLOCKS

The origin of hour – or sand – glasses is obscure. The Roman army may have used them to measure the night watches; another theory is that they are the invention of a French monk at the end of the 8th century. Charlemagne, king of the Franks (771–814), had a glass so big it only had to be turned over every 12 hours. Sand glasses were commonly used on board ships and were designed to run for 4 hours to match the spells of duty, which were called watches. Later the word 'watch' was borrowed to denote a small clock.

ABOVE: *This is a plaster cast of the Egyptian water clock dated about 1400 BC and found at Karnak Temple, Upper Egypt, in 1904. The original was made of alabaster and had a small hole in the base through which the water slowly dripped. As the water level fell, it moved down a time scale on the inside.*

Water clocks date back to Ancient Egypt and were most useful at night when a shadow clock was useless. There were still water clocks of a different kind in use in the 19th century, powered by the water wheels that also powered the machinery in mills and factories. When the water supply was reduced in dry spells, machinery slowed, as did production. The clock slowed too, so the workers found themselves working longer!

LEFT: *King Alfred used candles which burned for four hours to tell him the time, but they did not prevent him from burning the cakes! This one from the Science Museum in London is a copy of a typical Roman time candle. The numerals mark the hours as the candle burns.*

Ancient water clocks, sundials and sand glasses are analogue instruments producing a continuous movement of water, shadows or sand. Mechanical clocks marked the passage of time by a succession of regular pulses, which produced the idea of short time measurements such as the second, which could not be identified by analogue clocks. The imperceptible start-stop movement of a clock's hands makes them appear to be analogue devices and that is what they are called, as opposed to the handless digital clocks of today.

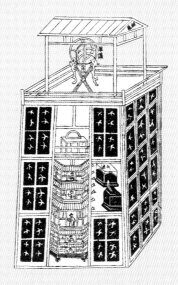

LEFT: Working model of a Chinese water clock. One of 36 scoops was filled every 24 seconds, when its weight tripped a lever. This pulled a chain which raised the balance lever, which in turn moved the driving wheel one notch. It was a very basic escapement system. The original wheel, built in 1088, drove an astronomical clock and used bells and figures to tell the time. A drawing of the clock is shown above.

ABOVE: These four glasses date from the beginning of the 18th century. They are designed to tell the quarter, half, three-quarter and full hour. The oldest illustration of an hour glass is that held in the hand of Temperance, one of the female figures in a fresco depicting good government painted by Lorenzetti in Sienna in 1339.

The first mechanical clocks were invented in the late 13th century. They were made of iron without bearings so suffered from friction, and metal expansion and contraction owing to temperature changes. They were driven by falling weights with their descent controlled by escapement devices, which required frequent manual adjustment. The weights themselves had to be regularly wound up, causing further time loss. These early clocks were inaccurate by 15–30 minutes a day and had to be set daily by a time-keeper using a sundial.

At first, clocks were made by blacksmiths and were intended only to ring bells to strike the hours in towers built on town halls, castles and churches. Clock dials with a single hand came in later in the 15th century, but it was well into the 17th century before clocks were accurate enough to use a minute hand.

BELOW: *The astronomical clock above Anne Boleyn's Gateway at Hampton Court was built for Henry VIII in 1540. It also showed the time of high tide at London Bridge, an important piece of information for those travelling down the River Thames.*

ABOVE: *This clock in Wells Cathedral is thought to date from 1392 and has an escapement which was up-dated in 1670. It continued to tell the cathedral time until 1835, but only the dial of the original clock is now in the cathedral: its mechanism ticks on, however, in the Science Museum in London.*

In the early 16th century, as travel became more common, the need for small clocks and even personal watches produced spring-driven mechanisms, but originally their tightly coiled springs made them run slower as they unwound. This problem was solved by Zech in 1525 using a principle first designed by Leonardo da Vinci. It consisted of a

length of chain or wire anchored to the main spring and wound round a grooved cone called a fusee. The spring and fusee not only made small clocks possible, but they could now be stood on shelves or in cases without having weights hanging below them.

But an even more revolutionary improvement to measuring time was the pendulum. Christiaan Huygens patented the first pendulum clock in 1657, and within a year spring-driven pendulum clocks were being made in quantity in Holland. They still needed an escapement, but the improvement in time-keeping was unprecedented, bringing accuracy down to within five minutes a day. Huygens later invented the spiral balance for watches. The first one, made in 1675, was accurate to within two minutes a day.

ABOVE: *Salisbury Cathedral clock dated 1386 is the oldest surviving clock in England. It is driven by a falling weight and strikes the hours but has no dial or hands. It rang a bell to call the monks to prayers.*

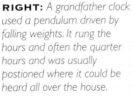

RIGHT: *A grandfather clock used a pendulum driven by falling weights. It rung the hours and often the quarter hours and was usually postioned where it could be heard all over the house.*

LEFT: *This is a reconstruction of the world's first astronomical clock, made by Giovanni Dondi in Italy in 1364. It is called astronomical because in addition to the usual mean time, it shows sidereal, or star, time and the movement of the Sun, the Moon and the five planets then known.*

Astronomical information interested educated people who studied the subject. The clocks were also status symbols for the wealthy; the more elaborate their functions, the greater the prestige.

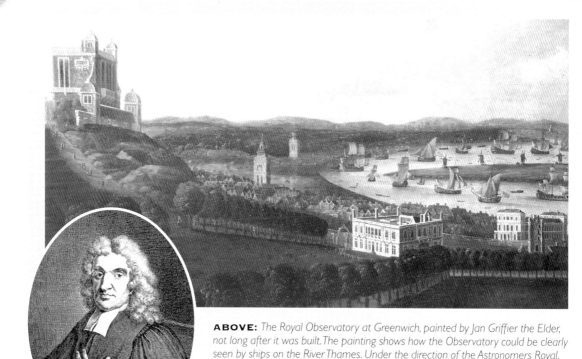

ABOVE: The Royal Observatory at Greenwich, painted by Jan Griffier the Elder, not long after it was built. The painting shows how the Observatory could be clearly seen by ships on the River Thames. Under the direction of the Astronomers Royal, the Royal Observatory grew into a complex of excellence for the observation of heavenly bodies.

ABOVE: John Flamsteed (1646–1719), the first Astronomer Royal.

ABOVE: Lines of longitude run from north to south. This 15th-century maritime map shows decorative ships and compasses with lines of latitude but no lines of longitude.

I n the 17th century, the mercantile countries of Europe were faced with the loss by shipwreck of thousands of ships, their crews and valuable cargoes, all because navigators had no method of finding their longitude. Without longitude, they had no way of knowing just how far east or west they were. Whichever country was first to solve the longitude problem would have an enormous advantage over its trading competitors. Astronomers believed that the answer would be found by observing the heavens and so Charles II commissioned Christopher Wren to build a Royal Observatory in his park at Greenwich, 'for finding out of the longitude of places for perfecting navigation and astronomy'. The building was completed by Christmas Day 1675.

The King appointed John Flamsteed, aged 28, as the first Astronomer Royal with the job of drawing up a map of the heavens accurate enough for astronomical navigation. To that purpose Flamsteed spent 43 years measuring the transits of the stars above him, but it was

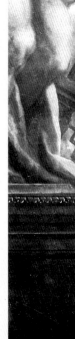

to take four more Astronomers Royal before Greenwich was able to publish the first comprehensive *Nautical Almanac* in 1776. This gave the angle between the Moon and certain fixed stars throughout the year, by which longitude could be calculated. The *Nautical Almanac* was complex and unpopular, taking up to three hours to work out an observational position. However, 100 years of work were virtually trumped by Harrison's nautical chronometer perfected the year before, although nautical almanacs have continued to be published ever since.

APECTUS INTRA CAMERAM STELLATAM

ABOVE: *The grandest part of the Royal Observatory was the Great Star Room, octagonal in shape with high windows all round to accommodate the long telescopes used in the 17th century. Unfortunately when Wren built the Observatory he did not align it exactly north-south on the true meridian so the work of observation was done in a shed in the garden! The exact position of the meridian was moved three times before being fixed in its present position.*

BELOW: *John Flamsteed and his assistant Thomas Weston are commemorated on the ceiling of the Painted Hall at Greenwich.*

Apr: 22
1715

THE GREENWICH MERIDIAN

The meridians of longitude circle the world north–south through the poles. By setting up a sight or telescope along a meridian the astronomer can watch the stars apparently revolving past that line and measure their position above it. By continual observation night after night over very long periods, a map can be built up of the night sky. That is what Flamsteed and his successors spent most of their night lives doing, and they eventually produced an accurate astronomical almanac for navigation, from which a ship's longitude position could be calculated anywhere in the world at any time of the year.

When the first *Nautical Almanac* was published it was based on observations on the present Greenwich main meridian, or 0°, that we know today. All time and distance east and west were calculated from that line on naval charts.

An engraving depicting the loss of Admiral Sir Clowdisley Shovell's fleet off the Scillies owing to a mistake in calculating longitude. This tragedy led to the government offering a £20,000 prize for the solution of the longitude problem.

On 22 October 1707 a naval fleet was sailing home from the Mediterranean when Admiral Sir Cloudisley Shovell miscalculated his meridian of longitude and drove the fleet onto the rocks off the Scilly Isles. The flag ship *Association* and three other warships were wrecked with the loss of 2,000 men. This navigational disaster, and the following pressure from influential merchants and sailors, resulted in the Act of 1714 which established a money prize of £20,000 (at least £1,000,000 today) 'to whoever develops a means of determining longitude with an error of no less than 0.5° during a voyage to and from the West Indies'. A further rider was that it had to be 'practicable and useful at sea'.

RIGHT: *H1 was John Harrison's first practical marine timekeeper. The wheels were made of oak, the rest of brass and other alloys. The spring drive was governed by a fusee, and all the moving parts were counter balanced by springs to make the mechanism independent of gravity. It was much admired by the scientific community and the Board of Longitude, but Harrison was sure he could do better.*

A Board of Longitude was set up to judge submissions, but it took more than half a century before the solution was found – by a self-taught clock-maker, John Harrison, who worked for 32 years to produce a clock which would keep near-perfect time under the climate changes of long voyages, and survive the buffeting, rolling and pitching of a ship in storm-tossed seas.

John Harrison was born in 1693, the son of a village carpenter in Foulby near Wakefield. At the age of 37 he went to the Observatory at Greenwich with secret plans for a sea clock to compete for the prize.

He was encouraged by the then Astronomer Royal, Edmond Halley, and helped financially by one of the world's leading clock-makers, George Graham. Harrison worked on his sea clock, called H1, for six years. It was the most

accurate time-keeper ever made. On returning to England after a trial voyage to Lisbon in 1736, Harrison correctly calculated that the ship was off The Lizard on the Penzance Peninsula and not, as all the officers on board believed, off Start Point, near Dartmouth, some 60 miles away to the north-east.

However, at a weight of 34kg and standing 63cm high it could hardly have been considered 'practicable and useful at sea'. Harrison felt he could improve it so the Board made him several payments on account to continue his research. Harrison moved to London where he found skilled craftsmen to make individual parts for him and started on a second chronometer, H2. It took him until January 1739 to make, but it had problems with its balance and Harrison did not allow it to be tested.

BELOW: *Harrison's second timekeeper, H2 was ready in 1739 but it was not a success.*

BELOW: *The many mad schemes suggested by people hoping to win the £20,000 prize inspired Hogarth to include two 'longitude maniacs' in his engravings of Bedlam, the asylum for the insane. Here one man is shown drawing on the wall while another gazes through a telescope.*

SUCCESS

Harrison worked for 19 years on H3 which included two brilliant inventions – a caged roller race, the forerunner of all modern machine ball bearings, and a bimetallic strip to even out expansion and contraction caused by temperature changes. It was the precursor of today's many temperature-sensitive control mechanisms. Unhappily he knew that his design had a fundamental flaw which would let it down in use. After all his hard work he decided that the answer lay simply in a totally different design.

Harrison changed tack and made his breakthrough with H4, which was not a clock but a watch. It contained bimetallic temperature compensation, an isochronous balance (its swings, large or small, took the same amount of time), and extensive use of jewels for bearings. Unlike his clocks it needed oil on its bearings. It was the forerunner of all precision watches and probably the most important timepiece ever made.

MEASURING LONGITUDE

74°
0°
74°W
Greenwich
New York
74°

The Earth rotates 360° every 24 hours, so local (solar) time changes by 4 minutes for every 1° of longitude. To find a ship's longitude, the navigator must compare the ship's local time with that of a chronometer set to Greenwich Mean Time. The difference between the two times shows how far east or west of 0° the ship is. All places on the same line of longitude make the same angle at the Earth's axis with the Greenwich meridian.

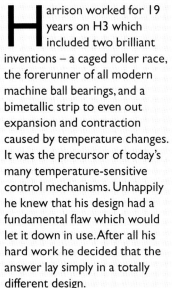

LEFT: *John Harrison (1693–1776) with his successful marine chronometer, H4.*

ABOVE: *H4 had a diameter of 13cm and weighed just 1.45kg. Harrison had realized that a watch with small high frequency oscillators, like the watch balance, was more stable when being carried about than earlier so-called portable clocks.*

T LAST

On trial in 1762 it was found to be accurate to 1 minute, 54 seconds in 147 days – an error of 0.0009 per cent.

The meridian problem was solved and from then on the navigational tool with which to find longitude was available to every navigator. Well, not immediately. It was too complex to be mass-produced and the Navy could not afford to supply it to their fleets. Only five years later a Frenchman modified and improved H4 and produced a cost-effective model which could be made in quantity. Harrison never saw the Frenchman's handiwork – he died on 24 March 1776, a very tired old man who had suffered the ignominy of having to petition George III to be paid £8,000, the balance owing to him out of the £20,000 prize money.

GLOBAL POSITIONING SYSTEM

Modern navigators use satellites instead of heavenly bodies to find their position. Two dozen satellites circling the world send encoded signals to Global Position System receivers and make computing position in the air, and on the sea or land, instant and foolproof. Small hand-held receivers like the Magellan GB receiver in the photo can give digital read-outs, at the push of a button, accurate to within 100 metres. Military versions can pinpoint positions to less than a metre. But any navigator would be wise to have a sextant and accurate chronometer, and know how to use them, in case the electric power fails or the batteries are flat.

HMS Centurion was the warship that carried John Harrison's H1 chronometer on its trial voyage to Lisbon in 1736. Unhappily the chronometer, although imperfect, was taken off the ship. In 1741 more than half her crew were dead or dying from hunger and exhaustion, after weeks of sailing back and forth through storms in the South Pacific without knowing their longitude. The ship survived and is painted here capturing the Covadonga on 20 June 1743.

GREEN

Until the Industrial Revolution clocks were run on local time which was set by looking at the local sundial. Because the world revolves on its axis the Sun appears to move from east to west across the sky, so that at any moment the shadows cast on sundials point to different times in different places at the rate of 4 minutes for each 1° going east or west. When it is noon at Greenwich the shadow on a sundial in Norwich will point to 12.05 and in Torquay to only 11.46. Time is always later in places east of you and earlier in those to the west.

Before railways, steam ships and telegraphic communications, the time difference between countries or within large countries was of little inconvenience. Travel was slow and one's timepiece would need only slight adjustment from one day to another. For example, it takes the noontime Sun a mere 12 minutes to move from Boston to New York but in the early 19th century a traveller would adjust the time difference between the two cities over a period of three to four days. Experienced travellers kept timetables of places they visited or wore watches with two minute hands, one showing home time, the other set to the time of their destination.

BELOW: *In 1833 a large ball was erected above Flamsteed House at the Royal Observatory, Greenwich, to be a visual time signal for ships on the Thames. At 12.55 hours it rose halfway up the mast, at 12.58 hours it rose to the top, and at exactly 13.00 hours it dropped – at which moment navigators on the river could set their chronometers to Greenwich Mean Time.*

ABOVE: *In 1852 the master clock-maker, Charles Shepherd, installed a great electric master clock in the Royal Observatory which sent impulses to slave clocks throughout the country. That clock is still working, and the public can check Greenwich Mean Time by its nearest slave clock at the main entrance to the Observatory.*

With the coming of the railways it was necessary to have accurate timetables with every town and station using the same time and the invention of the electric telegraph made this possible. The Observatory at Greenwich set up an electric master clock in 1852 to send out time pulses along telegraph wires to other clocks around the country, giving Greenwich Mean Time (GMT).

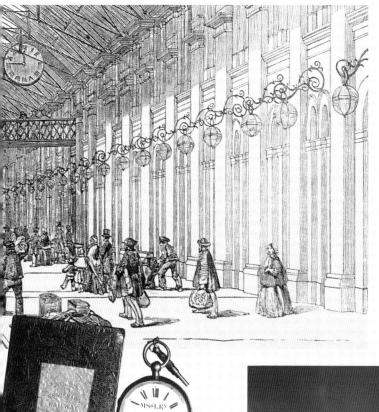

LEFT: *Birmingham Station in 1854. The station clock would have been set to Greenwich Mean Time, since two years earlier the Royal Observatory at Greenwich started sending time pulses along the telegraph wires to all parts of the country.*

BELOW: *Visitors to Greenwich after sunset will see a fine green laser beam piercing the night sky and may think it is some form of illumination. In fact it is an aerial representation of the Greenwich meridian aimed due south from the heart of the Royal Observatory. As a line of light in the sky it is like the imaginary longitude line drawn through Greenwich on maps.*

ABOVE: *A pocket watch used by a guard in about 1870 and a copy of the first edition of Bradshaw's Railway Companion of 1840, which gave 'the times of departures and fares etc for the railways of England'.*

In the mid-19th century European railway systems worked to the time of the capital cities within any one country, but in the United States it would have been hopeless to use Washington DC time to cover a country which from east to west had a time difference of 3.5 hours. In 1883 a plan was put into operation by the railways dividing the country into Eastern, Central and Pacific Standard Times.

As soon as submarine cables were established across the Atlantic, across the Channel and from Europe to India it was time to organize a world system of time zones. In October 1884 it was agreed that the 0° Greenwich meridian, already on the nautical charts used by 75 per cent of the world's shipping, should be the single world meridian from which all longitude east or west up to 180° would be calculated.

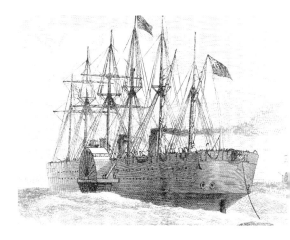

ABOVE: *The Great Eastern laying the Atlantic telegraph cable in 1865. The laying was completed in 1866, and on 27 July a message was transmitted from Queen Victoria at Osborne House to President Andrew Johnson in Washington.*

INTERNATIONAL TIME ZONES

The world is divided into 24 time zones each spanning 15°. In places the lines dividing zones are slightly adjusted to avoid bisecting countries. As you travel west you put your watch back one hour every time you cross a zone line and when travelling east you add an hour. The international date-line is at 180°. If you cross it going west you put your watch back one hour but put your calendar one day forward, and the opposite if crossing the date-line going east.

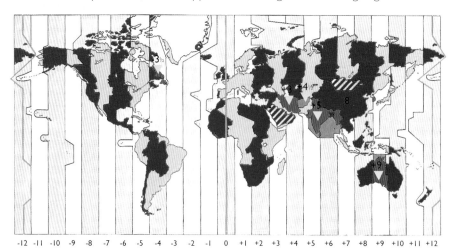

Local Times

-12 -11 -10 -9 -8 -7 -6 -5 -4 -3 -2 -1 0 +1 +2 +3 +4 +5 +6 +7 +8 +9 +10 +11 +12

Geochronology is the branch of geology concerned with dating the events of the Earth's evolution. Scientists estimate that the solar system including Earth was formed between 4.5 and 5 billion years ago (about 10 billion years after the Big Bang). From the early 1800s geologists studied the fossil remains in sedimentary rocks to determine the relative ages and duration of geological eras.

Since the mid-1920s radiometric dating has provided absolute age data to supplement relative dates obtained from fossil records and has made it possible to quantify the geological scale as far back as the oldest rocks, more than 3.9 billion years old.

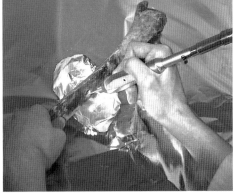

ABOVE: *This scientist is taking a piece from a reindeer's bone for dating by radiocarbon techniques.*

BELOW: *Archaeologists use layers in sedimentary rocks to help them date prehistoric remains. Erosion of this bank in County Sligo, Ireland, has exposed a large prehistoric midden with layers of oyster shells, charcoal deposits and burnt stones. The layers give a relative time to within a few hundred years, but radiocarbon dating would provide an absolute date.*

All rocks contain radioactive isotopes that slowly decay at a constant rate, enabling scientists to determine their age. Uranium changes slowly into lead and, by measuring the amount of lead in uranium ore, scientists can calculate when the rock was formed. Another clue to geological time is radioactive carbon (carbon 14) which has a half life of only 5,700 years and is absorbed by all plants and animals. The rate of the carbon's decay tells you how long ago the specimen died.

BELOW: *A fossil starfish cast in the rocks during the Jurassic period, about 140 million years ago.*

MODERN

In the 19th century Britain's overseas trade brought wealth and greater spending power to many more people. Relatively cheap domestic clocks came on the market, the most common being in wooden cases imported from Germany and America. As soon as an artisan, farmer or shopkeeper had a little money saved he would buy a clock, set it on the mantelpiece and invite the neighbours to come in and watch it.

The First World War increased the use of wrist watches, which had been unfashionable for men until they became standard issue for officers. Summer Time was introduced in 1916, so adjusting time to the interests of industrial production. The first experimental electric clocks had been invented as early as 1840, and came into popular production after William Shortt produced his Free Pendulum Clock in 1921. It was accurate to a few thousandths of a second and was used at the Royal Observatory, Greenwich.

The quartz clock was invented in 1929, accurate to about 1/100th of a second a day, but was inaccurate compared to the atomic clock built at the National Bureau of Standards, Washington, in 1948–49. In 1955 the first one built at the National Physical Laboratory, Teddington, London, was

ABOVE: *The first atomic clock made by the National Physical Laboratory in Teddington, in 1955.*

BELOW LEFT: *As clocks became ever more accurate and practical, they brought about greater social cohesion: the courts, universities, businesses and manufacturers could run their affairs to proper timetables and avoid wasting time. By the mid-19th century factories were manned around the clock and the railways ran to strict timetables. Shops like that shown here did brisk trade. Today more than ever, time rules our lives.*

TIME

ABOVE: *This Art Deco electric digital clock was made in the United States in 1930. The numbers are not shown by lighted crystals as in today's digital clocks, but by changing cards. The clock is made of Bakelite, the first kind of synthetic plastic.*

ABOVE RIGHT: *By the time this space shuttle took off from Kennedy Space Center in 1990, space launches had become routine. Yet the space program could not have been developed without the absolute accuracy of time and direction provided by atomic clocks and computers.*

LEFT: *Quartz, like this, is found naturally in the rocks and is mined in Cornwall and Devon, but the crystals used in clocks and watches are specially grown in the laboratory.*

accurate to within one second in 300 years. The current best atomic clocks are accurate to one second in 3 million years.

Atomic clocks are now used for high-speed navigation in jet planes and in the guidance systems of ballistic and nuclear missiles: atomic time no longer worries about the Sun or Moon, but sends its signals from an atomic clock at the Bureau International de l'Heure which averages those of some 80 atomic clocks around the world. GMT has been superseded by UTC (Co-ordinated Universal Time) from Paris. The cheap and cheerful digital watches which people wear now are more accurate than the expensive Rolex of a few decades ago and would have served Raleigh, Columbus and Sir Clowdisley Shovell well as marine chronometers.

RIGHT: *A modern quartz watch.*

So inconceivable is the size of the Universe that to give distances in miles would produce intolerably long strings of zeros. Instead distances are calculated in light-years – for in one year light travels approximately six million million miles – itself a slightly indigestible figure!

To get some conception of light-year distances, consider that light could travel seven times round the Earth in a second, that the Sun is 500 light-seconds from the Earth and that the nearest star to us, after the Sun, is Proxima Centauri, 4.3 light-years off, or a staggering 26,000,000,000,000 miles away.

The Milky Way, which curves across the night sky, is a huge disc of a myriad stars with a diameter of 100,000 light-years. There are millions and millions more such galaxies out in the Universe, each with millions of Suns. In 1993 the furthest visible galaxy was calculated to be about 14 billion light-years from the Earth.

From these figures it is clear that the cosmonaut of the future would have to travel close to the speed of light to get to and from anywhere worthwhile, let alone another galaxy, during his own lifetime. Such speeds can never be attained since, as Einstein propounded back in 1905, nothing can accelerate past the speed of light because, at that speed, an object's length would reach zero and its mass would become infinite. It would require an infinite amount of energy to accelerate anything to the speed of light.

BELOW: *This photo of the central region of our galaxy, the Milky Way, was taken from Australia in 1986. The light from many of these stars has taken 30,000 years to reach us.*

SCALE OF TIME EVENTS

Age of known Universe	12–15 billion years
Age of our solar system	4.5 billion years
Time for our Sun to complete one journey around the Milky Way galaxy	225 million years
Time for light to reach us from the centre of our galaxy	about 30,000 years
Time since the dinosaurs died out	64 million years
Time since the earliest humanoids	3 million years
Time since the last Ice Age	10,000 years

The brightest star in this photo is Sirius, the Dog Star, in the constellation of Canis Major. At 8.7 light-years away from Earth, it is one of our nearest stars and is the brightest star in the night sky.

CAN TIME VANISH DOWN A HOLE?

A black hole is a giant Sun which has exhausted its internal thermonuclear fuels, become unstable and collapsed inward upon itself. The weight of matter falling in from all directions compresses the dying star to a point of near zero volume and infinite density. A black hole produced by a collapsed Sun three times larger than our own would end up with a radius of only 30km. The velocity needed for matter to escape from the gravitational pull within a black hole would have to be greater than the speed of light, so nothing – no matter, no radiation, nor light – can escape from it into space.

They are very difficult to observe because they are so small and they emit no light. If they cannot be seen how are they found? Their exis-tence is only betrayed by the effect of their peripheral gravitational fields on nearby matter which, while being sucked towards the hole, becomes super-heated and radiates powerful X-rays before disappearing for ever. In 1994 the Hubble Space Telescope produced evidence of an unbelievably massive black hole in the M87 galaxy: it has the mass of two to three billion Suns but is no larger than our solar system. Its existence is marked by its effect on an envelope of gas swirling round it at incredible velocity.

ABOVE: *A computer image of a black hole. Some scientists have postulated that a worm hole, formed when two black holes in different parts of space join up, could provide a shortcut through space-time.*

TIME IN SPACE

Whenever we look at the stars we are looking at the past. With telescopes we can see galaxies as they looked millions of years ago and analyse the colour spectrums of stars which died before there was life on Earth. A very advanced civilization may well be looking now at our world as it was in the age of the dinosaur, or maybe they have just observed the volcanic eruption of Vesuvius or the atomic flash of Hiroshima.

Time never stops and we cannot overtake it but we can see it coming from the past. Perhaps if there were a suitable 'mirror' hanging in precisely the right position in space, and had we the technology, tomorrow we could watch the building of the pyramids or see the shape of the continents when they were still joined together. If there are intelligent life-forms out there, they may be too distant to have yet detected life on our planet.

RIGHT: *The Hubble Space Telescope first launched in 1990 has allowed astronomers to look deep into space without the distortion produced by our own atmosphere. Hubble has sent back pictures of exploding superstars and events that must have happened close in time to the Big Bang itself.*

MAIN PICTURE: *This image from the Hubble Space Telescope shows many very distant galaxies. The bluer objects are generally younger or closer and the redder objects are older or farther away.*

LOOKING I

THE END OF TIME?

Time is marked by change, one moment to the next. But if change stopped would time go on regardless? Here is one theory.

The laws of thermodynamics tell us that energy in the form of heat passes from hot matter to colder matter, but cannot pass back the other way. Over many billions of years this could result in the averaging out of energy differences, called entropy. If the Universe were to reach maximum entropy with nothing hotter or colder than anything else, there would be no exchange of energy, so no change and, therefore, no time.

Another theory is that one day the Universe may stop expanding and start collapsing back on itself. Galaxies would merge with each other until there was only one enormous galaxy which would in turn contract, get even hotter and the Universe would become a blue incandescent ball, returning to its original state before the Big Bang. Would the Universe then cease to exist, or would it expand again and create new worlds? Would time start all over again?

ACKNOWLEDGEMENTS

Photographs are reproduced with permission of the following:

The Ancient Art & Architecture Collection: 4 left, 6 top; Heather Angel: 3 below right; Bridgeman Art Library: front cover centre left, 2 below left, 6–7, 13 centre; The British Museum: 7 below right, 17 below right; Mary Evans Picture Library: 2 top, 6 below left, 8 top left, 20–21, 24 below left; Mary Evans Picture Library/Explorer Archives: 7 top, 14 below left; Giraudon/Bridgeman Art Library: front cover below centre; Magellan Corporation: 19 top; Mirror Syndication International: 11 top (from Joseph Needham, Science and Civilisation in China, Vol. IV Part 2, Cambridge University Press 1965); National Maritime Museum London: 14 top, 15 top, 16 top, 16 below, 17 top, 18–19, 19 below, 21 below right; The Natural History Museum, London: 23 below right, 24–25; Pitkin Unichrome: 9 right, 12 top, 13 top (photo Peter Smith), 25 below right (photo Mark Slade); By kind permission of the Commander of the Royal Naval College, Greenwich: 14–15; Science Photo Library: front cover top background and 26 (Ronald Royer), front cover below background, inside front cover and 3 top (Julian Baum), 23 top (James King-Holmes), 25 top right and 28 inset (NASA), 26 inset (John Sanford), 27 and back cover (Erich Schrempp), 28–29 (Space Telescope Science Institute/NASA); Science & Society Picture Library/National Railway Museum: 21 below left; Science & Society Picture Library/Science Museum: front cover centre, centre right and below right, 2–3, 8 top right, 8 below left, 10 top, 10 below left, 10–11, 11 below right, 13 below, 14 centre, 18 left, 24 top, 25 top left; John Watney: front cover centre background, 4–5, 5 top, 5 below, 12 below, 20 top left, 20 below, 23 below left; John Watney Vintage Pictures: 8–9, 22 top; Guy Whitworth: 9 top left; Inside pages corner detail Science Photo Library/Ronald Royer and John Watney.

Written by John Watney.
Illustrations on pages 18 and 22 by Roger Hutchins.
Edited by Angela Royston.
Designed by Nick Avery.
Picture research by Christine Crawshaw.
The publishers would like to thank Dave Rooney for reading the text.

Printed in Great Britain
ISBN 0 85372 921 2   1/99

Time passes inexorably from moment to moment. We are usually so busy keeping up with time – catching trains, meeting schedules, getting to school or work – that we have no time to stop and think about time itself. This book looks at some of the big questions ...

- **DID TIME BEGIN WHEN THE UNIVERSE BEGAN – WITH THE BIG BANG?**
- **DOES TIME PROCEED AT A CONSTANT PACE?**
- **CAN TIME VANISH DOWN A BLACK HOLE?**
- **WILL TIME EVER END?**

and also looks at advances and mishaps in the long history of measuring time and making clocks ...

- **HOW AN ERROR IN THE ROMAN CALENDAR MISPLACED EASTER INTO SUMMER.**
- **JOHN HARRISON'S LONG STRUGGLE TO INVENT A TIME-KEEPER THAT COULD BE USED TO MEASURE LONGITUDE AND SO WIN A PRIZE OF £20,000.**
- **HOW GREENWICH BECAME THE STANDARD FOR INTERNATIONAL TIME.**

PITKIN

ISBN 0-85372-921-2

9 780853 729211